The Very Best o

Vernon Scannell was born in Spilsby, Lincolnshire in 1922 and educated at Queens Park School, Aylesbury, Bucks, and the University of Leeds. He served with the Gordon Highlanders in the Second World War, in the Middle East and in Normandy where he was wounded.

His awards for literature include the Heinemann Award (1960) and Cholmondeley Services to Literature in 1981. In 1961 he was elected a Fellow of the Royal Society of Literature.

He has been a boxer, a teacher of English and, since 1962, he has worked as a freelance writer, reviewer and broadcaster. His published poetry includes several collections for younger readers, including *The Apple-Raid* (1974), *The Clever Potato* (1988), *Love Shouts and Whispers* (1990) and *Travelling Light* (1991). He has also written about his own life in three volumes of autobiography. In 2000, a new collection of his poetry was published, *Views and Distance*, and a novel for adults, *Feminine Endings*. Vernon Scannell has four grown-up children, three grandchildren and two dogs. He lives in Yorkshire.

Brett Hudson lives in Hove, Sussex, where he has been painting and illustrating for over five years. During that time, he has illustrated many projects, including a medical publication, greetings cards, and several well-known magazines.

Brett's style and sense of fun is well-suited to children's stories and poetry.

Also available from Macmillan Children's Books

The Very Best of Richard Edwards
The Very Best of Ian McMillan

We Couldn't Provide Fish Thumbs
Poems by Vernon Scannell, James Berry,
Judith Nicholls, Grace Nichols and Matthew Sweeney

Coming Soon

The Very Best of Paul Cookson
The Very Best of Wes Magee
The Very Best of David Harmer

THE VERY BEST OF...

VERNON SCANNELL

A Book of Poems

Illustrated by Brett Hudson

MACMILLAN CHILDREN'S BOOKS

For my grandchildren, Harry, Lottie and Hugh

First published 2001 by Macmillan Children's Books
a division of Macmillan Publishers Limited
25 Eccleston Place, London SW1W 9NF
Basingstoke and Oxford
www.macmillan.com

Associated companies throughout the world

ISBN 0 330 48344 7

1 3 5 7 9 8 6 4 2

A CIP catalogue record for this book is available from
the British Library.

Typeset by Macmillan Children's Books
Printed and bound in Great Britain by Mackays of Chatham plc, Kent

Contents

Introduction

Once I would have thought that Boxing and Poetry were an odd mixture. That was before I met Vernon Scannell. He began boxing and writing as a boy and both became important. When I first talked to him about boxing he reminded me that John Keats, Lord Byron, T.S. Eliot and Bernard Shaw – four great writers – were also interested in the sport. He says he was 'a good amateur' which is modest for someone who, aged 14, was a finalist in the Schoolboy Boxing Championships of Great Britain and later Captain of Boxing at Leeds University and Cruiser-Weight Champion of Northern Universities. He once 'sparred' with the great Freddie Mills, and for a while travelled with a fairground-boxing booth. In a poem from his adult collection, called 'Mastering the Craft', he describes the boxer's necessary skills and says:

'The same with poets: they must train,
Practise metre's footwork, learn
The old iambic left and right,
To change the pace and how to hold
The big punch till the proper time,
Jab away with accurate rhyme;
Adapt the style or be knocked cold.
But first the groundwork must be done.
Those poets who have never learnt
The first moves of the game, they can't
Hope to win. . .'

Writing on 'What is Poetry' he said that 'Poetry is a special way of using words, and any interference with the selection and order of those words will destroy it.' He cares about the proper use of language, dislikes tattered or outworn clichés, crude handling of metre and rhyme. I like the way he describes words as not 'static counters' but 'living, changing things, each with its own colour, texture, weight and flavour'.

My curiosity about writers' early lives led me to Vernon Scannell's autobiography, *Drums of Morning*, where he describes a far from easy childhood. He and his brother, Kenneth, he writes, suffered quite brutal punishments from their father:

> *The childhood treats of toffees, chocolate or any kind of confectionery were virtually unknown to Kenneth and me so we were rendered speechless with joy and anticipation when Father called us from the back yard, where we had been playing, to come into the kitchen-living-room where he had placed on the table a half-pound slab of wrapped milk chocolate.*
>
> *'All right,' he said to Kenneth, 'you open it. You can have half each.'*
>
> *Kenneth, who could scarcely believe that he was not dreaming, picked up the slab of chocolate and removed the shiny blue outer wrapping and paused before tearing off the silver paper.*
>
> *'Go on!' Father urged, clearly at least as excited as we were.*
>
> *Kenneth tore off the silver paper. For a moment we both felt a sick incomprehension. The 'chocolate' was made of wood. It was a shop-window display model of the real thing. Kenneth and I said nothing as we heard our father's prodigious laughter and saw his wild, excited eyes. For us it had been too good to be true anyway. So we went back to our play in*

the yard, refusing to show our disappointment, instinctively colluding to minimise his triumphant pleasure in our discomfiture. But we were never to forget.

This incident might well have formed the subject for a poem. The heightened excitement, build-up of events and the bleak ending are present in many Scannell poems. He is expert at the twist, the 'sting in the tail', and it stays with you; you find yourself re-reading poems, discovering more each time.

When the family moved from Beeston, near Nottingham, to Aylesbury, Bucks, in 1931, Vernon and Ken went to Queen's Park Boys' School, described as 'bearable but hardly inspiring'. As well as beatings from his father's strap at home, at school there was Mr Gunstone, who once, when no one would own up to having thrown an apple core at his head, gave all 36 boys in the class six strokes of the cane, three on each hand.

It was here that Vernon began writing. English lessons were the most enjoyable, although the master chose boring subjects for compositions: 'A Day in the Life of a Postman', 'A Windy Day', 'My Favourite Hobby'. This may have encouraged Vernon towards memorable titles for his poems: 'Flying a Camel', 'The Clever Potato', 'Incendiary', 'Beauty of Boats'.

Along with boxing, writing and reading occupied much of his spare time, when he wasn't in charge of his small sister, Sylvia. When he was aged about 10 he remembers reading two books by Edgar Wallace, *The Four Just Men* and *The Green Archer*, but had even greater pleasure from the comic, 'The Magnet', in which Billy Bunter and Harry Wharton of 'The Famous Five' appeared.

Poetry was not a major interest at school, mainly

because the least interesting was chosen to be learnt by heart or copied in best handwriting as a punishment. It was *The Methuen Anthology of Modern Verse* that led him to the work of Thomas Hardy, Edward Thomas, Wilfred Owen, Walter de la Mare and Charlotte Mew. 'I believe it was not a bad introduction to the art of poetry,' he wrote. I agree, because it was my experience too.

In 1938 he wrote a poem that convinced him that one day he would be a poet. It was called 'The Day that Summer Died'. Later he returned to it, re-worked it, and you will find it in this collection. It is tempting to read a writer's own experiences into poems and stories. Was Vernon Scannell, perhaps, the narrator in 'The Apple-Raid'?

Well, partly he was – in his autobiography we hear of his friend, Eddie, and how 'in the early darkness of Autumn nights we went scrumping in the orchards of posh houses . . .'; the idea grows from that. Was he the child of one of my favourite poems, 'Hide and Seek'? Did he have a colour-blind 'Uncle Edward'? Surely he is the nervous young boxer in 'First Fight'?

There is a great deal more to discover about this poet who has been, in a packed and varied life, a teacher and lecturer, a soldier in the Second World War, a lover of dogs and the father of a family.

'Liquorice Allsorts' reveals him as being, like me, fond of those sweets, and the end of the poem might well describe the contents of this collection:

> 'a treasury of flavours;
> bitter-sweet colours.'

Anne Harvey

Poem on Bread

The poet is about to write a poem;
He does not use a pencil or a pen.
He dips his long thin finger into jam
Or something savoury preferred by men.
This poet does not choose to write on paper;
He takes a single slice of well-baked bread
And with his jam or marmite-nibbed forefinger
He writes his verses down on that instead.
His poem is fairly short as all the best are.
When he has finished it he hopes that you
Or someone else – your brother, friend or sister –
Will read and find it marvellous and true.
If you can't read, then eat: it tastes quite good.
If you do neither, all that I can say
Is he who needs no poetry or bread
Is really in a devilish bad way.

The Clever Potato

Over sixty years ago
A boy of five would walk to school;
Sometimes in the falling snow
Of winter mornings, past the pool,
Frozen white like shrouded glass,
Along Peel's Lane a mile almost
Between pale fields of brittle grass,
Arriving like a little ghost
In Mrs Wiscombe's infant class.

She did not understand why he
Often cried when he got there.
His hands were cold, he said, but she
Did not know that, like a pair
Of coals his fingers burnt, then froze.
She said, 'Tell Mum or Dad to get
Warmer gloves for you than those.'
At home his granny cried, 'Oh pet,
You should have told us this before!
I've got the very thing for you!'
Next morning Granny, at the door,
Said, 'Wear your gloves and take this too.
Hold it in both hands, and your
Fingers will not feel the cold.'
And what she handed him was one
Baked potato, firm and gold
From the oven. 'Better run
Or you'll be late,' his granny said.
'What do I do when I get there?'
He asked.

'You eat it up instead
Of taking lunch for playtime, dear.
You love potatoes. So you see
What clever things potatoes do,
They warm your hands and they can be
A tasty snack. If hungry, you
Can eat your muff!'

Dear reader, who
Did this story happen to?
And am I sure that it is true?
Well yes, I'm sure because, you see,
The boy who ate his muff was me.

Mother's Milk

Shortly after John began
To go to school his brother Jake,
Two years older, said to John
During Monday morning break:
'Guess what! I've got amazing news!
When you go home to have your tea
You'll find a stranger in the house.
I promise you! Just wait and see!'

So after school, John hurried home
To see what Jake was on about;
And what he found astonished him
So much he gave a squeaky shout
And then he yelled, 'Oh Mum! What's that?'

'Not *what* is that but *who*,' she smiled,
And looked down where, upon her lap,
She nursed a tiny newborn child.

'This is Toby,' Mother said.
'You've got another brother, dear!'
John thought at first that he would like
To see the creature disappear.
But very soon his feelings changed;
He found he liked the babe instead
Of feeling jealous, and he loved
To watch him bathed and changed and fed.

A few weeks later, John came home
After school and said, 'Today
We were told that cows eat grass,
And grass turns into milk. But hey!
What I want to know is this—'
He frowned with puzzled eyes at Mother –
'I've never seen you eating grass,
How come you've milk to feed my brother?'

Jelly-lover

Jill likes stuff that wobbles, quivers,
Trembles and gives little shivers,
Ripples, promising rich pleasure,
Glitters like Aladdin's treasure,
Green or red or orange, yellow,
Sharp and fruity, sweet and mellow.
Jill likes jelly in her belly,
She would eat it from a welly;
Loves to see it shake and shudder,
Brightly joggle, jounce and judder.
She adores its slippery motion
And could wallow in an ocean,
Not of green and foamy briny
But lime jelly, smooth and shiny.
Jill, whose best friend calls her Jilly,
Said, 'I hope I don't sound silly
If I say my dream vacation
Has to be an invitation
To an island, gold and shining,
Where I'd spend all day reclining
By a sprinkling sherbet fountain
Shaded by a jelly mountain.'

Sweet Song

For Nancy and Jane

This is the sweet song,
Song of all the sweets,
Caramel and butterscotch,
Bulls-eyes, raspberry treats;

Treacle toffee, acid drops,
Pastilles, crystal fruits,
Bubble gum and liquorice sticks
As black as new gumboots;

Peppermint creams and aniseed balls,
Tiny sweets and whoppers,
Dolly mixtures, chocolate drops,
Gigantic gobstoppers;

Lemon sherbets, jelly babies,
Chocolate cream and flake,
Nougat, fudge, and sweets that give
You tooth and belly ache.

But the sweets I end my song with
Could never give me pain
In tooth or tummy – anywhere.
One's Nancy; one is Jane.

Liquorice Allsorts

Shiny, solid, black
cylinder; tiny topper;
hat without a brim.

Little round cushion
wholly covered by hundreds
of purple pinheads.

Small black length of hose
totally filled with close-packed
perfectly smooth snow.

Cubic sandwiches,
white or coloured, with fillings
like black postage stamps.

A coconut ruff;
thick wheel of pink or yellow
with ebony hub.

Mix all together;
a treasury of flavours;
bitter-sweet colours.

Intelligence Test

'What do you use your eyes for?'
The white-coated man inquired.
'I use my eyes for looking,'
Said Toby, ' – unless I'm tired.'

'I see. And then you close them,'
Observed the white-coated man.
'Well done. A very good answer.
Let's try another one.

'What is your nose designed for?
What use is the thing to you?'
'I use my nose for smelling,'
Said Toby, 'don't you, too?'

'I do indeed,' said the expert,
'That's what the thing is for.
Now I've another question to ask you,
Then there won't be any more.

'What are your ears intended for?
Those things at each side of your head?
Come on – don't be shy – I'm sure you can say.'
'For washing behind,' Toby said.

The Gift

When Jonathan was almost six years old
He found a most exciting game to play:
The clothes-pegs that his mother kept to hold
The linen chorus firm on washing day
Were not the kind that snap with little jaws
Like tiny crocodiles: her wooden pegs
Were of the type that gypsies make, and more
Fun to play with. Each had two thin legs
To grip the line, a body, small round head
On narrow shoulders. Jonathan began
To play with one, and when his sister said,
'What's that you've got?' He said, 'A wooden man,
A soldier. Look, I've got a regiment.'
For hours, quite happily, he marched and drilled
His wooden army; then he sternly sent
Them out to fight, to triumph or be killed.
His parents watched his game and, for the day
That he was six, they brought him home a treat –
A box of soldiers, some in German grey,
Some in British khaki, all complete
With weapons and equipment. He'd no need
To use those wooden clothes-pegs any more.
He thanked them for his soldiers and agreed
That they were just the troops to wage a war.
They heard him later, marshalling his men;
The noise came from his bedroom. They crept there
To see the joy their present gave him. When
They peeped inside, the sight that met their stare
Amazed them both; for Jonathan had spread
The clothes-pegs on his carpet for the fray;

The birthday gift was packed beneath his bed,
Neat in its box. The parents stole away.
'Why does he still use those?' the father said.
The mother's smile was one that lights and warms:
'Because they have such splendid uniforms.'

Nettles

My son aged three fell in the nettle bed.
'Bed' seemed a curious name for those green spears,
That regiment of spite behind the shed:
It was no place for rest. With sobs and tears
The boy came seeking comfort and I saw
White blisters beaded on his tender skin.
We soothed him till his pain was not so raw.
At last he offered us a watery grin,
And then I took my hook and honed the blade
And went outside and slashed in fury with it
Till not a nettle in that fierce parade
Stood upright any more. Next task: I lit
A funeral pyre to burn the fallen dead.
But in two weeks the busy sun and rain
Had called up tall recruits behind the shed:
My son would often feel sharp wounds again.

Cat

My cat has got no name,
We simply call him Cat;
He doesn't seem to blame
Anyone for that.

For he is not like us
Who often, I'm afraid,
Kick up quite a fuss
If *our* names are mislaid.

As if, without a name,
We'd be no longer there
But like a tiny flame
Vanish in bright air.

My pet, he doesn't care
About such things as that:
Black buzz and golden stare
Require no name but Cat.

Burying Moses

Moses was very old,
Ninety-eight, my grandpa said,
So we shouldn't cry too much
Now poor old Moses was dead.

Moses used to be black
But he slowly turned grey as a fog,
And snuffled and wheezed and snored.
Moses was our old dog.

Each year that people live
Counts for a dog as seven.
'He was a good old boy,' said Grandpa.
'He's sure to go to heaven.

'But first we must go and bury him
At the back of the garden shed,
So come and give me a hand;
We'll make him a deep warm bed.'

So then we lowered old Moses
Down in the hole Grandpa dug,
And he huddled there in a bundle
Like a dusty old fireside rug.

Then we filled in the hole and patted
The soil down smooth and flat.
'I'll make a cross,' said Grandpa.
'The least we can do is that.

'He'll be wagging his tail in heaven,
So you mustn't be too upset . . .'
But Grandpa's voice sounded croaky,
And I could see his old cheeks were wet.

My Dog

My dog belongs to no known breed,
   A bit of this and that.
His head looks like a small haystack;
   He's lazy, smelly, fat.

If I say, 'Sit!' he walks away.
   When I throw stick or ball
He flops down in the grass as if
   He had no legs at all.

Then looks at me with eyes that say,
   'You threw the thing, not me.
You want it back? Then get it back.
   Fair's fair, you must agree.'

He is a thief. Last week but one
   He stole the Sunday roast
And showed no guilt at all as we
   Sat down to beans on toast.

The only time I saw him run –
   And he went like a flash –
Was when a mugger in the park
   Tried to steal my cash.

My loyal brave companion flew
　　Like a missile to the gate
And didn't stop till safely home.
　　He left me to my fate.

And would I swap him for a dog
　　Obedient, clean and good,
An honest, faithful, lively chap?
　　Oh boy, I would, I would!

Uncle Albert

When I was almost eight years old
My Uncle Albert came to stay;
He wore a watch-chain made of gold
And sometimes he would let me play
With both the chain and gleaming watch,
And though at times I might be rough
He never seemed to bother much.
He smelled of shaving soap and snuff.
To me he was a kind of god,
Immensely wise and strong and kind,
And so I thought it rather odd
When I came home from school to find
Two strangers, menacing and tall,
In the parlour, looking grim
As Albert – suddenly quite small –
Let them rudely hustle him
Out to where a black car stood.
Both Albert and his watch and chain
Disappeared that day for good.
My parents said he'd gone to Spain.

Uncle Edward's Affliction

Uncle Edward was colour-blind;
We grew accustomed to the fact.
When he asked someone to hand him
The green book from the window-seat
And we observed its bright red cover
Either apathy or tact
Stifled comment. We passed it over.
Much later, I began to wonder
What curious world he wandered in,
Down streets where pea-green pillar-boxes
Grinned at a fire-engine as green;
How Uncle Edward's sky at dawn
And sunset flooded marshy green.
Did he ken John Peel with his coat so green
And Robin Hood in Lincoln Red?
On country walks avoid being stung
By nettles hot as a witch's tongue?
What meals he savoured with his eyes:
Green strawberries and fresh red peas,
Green beef and greener burgundy.
All unscientific, so it seems:
His world was not at all like that,
So those who claim to know have said.
Yet, I believe, in war-smashed France
He must have crawled from neutral mud
To lie in pastures dark and red
And seen, appalled, on every blade
The rain of innocent green blood.

Epitaph for a Gifted Man

He was not known among his friends for wit;
He owned no wealth, nor did he crave for it.
His looks would never draw a second glance;
He could not play an instrument or dance,
Or sing, or paint, nor would he ever write
The music, plays, or poems that delight
And win the whole world's worship and applause.
He did not fight for any noble cause;
Showed neither great extravagance nor thrift;
But he loved greatly: that was his one gift.

White

Inside the coconut's brown case
    The flesh is moist and white
And you will find it crunchy, sweet,
    When you take a bite.

White clouds across the blue sky float
    And on the lake below
The swans, as in a looking-glass,
    Drift just as white and slow.

But in the fields the daisies' shy
    White petals seem to know
There is no white that pleases quite
    As much as early snow.

That silent fall that changes all
    Within a single night
And in the morning shows a new
    World of perfect white.

Riding Home

Sweet salt of frost is tingling in the air;
Grey daylight withers and the darkening sky
Is freckled with faint stars as we now share
This simple happiness, old Meg and I,
A bliss composed of pleasant weariness
And recollections of the day's long ride.
I am eager for the silk caress
Of warm and scented water once inside
The house, whose lighted windows I now see,
But Meg must first be stabled, brushed and fed.
I love to do this and I think that she
Knows I do. Already, in my head,
I see the lamplit stable, sniff the hay
Mingled with the leathery smells of tack,
And suddenly Meg gives a little neigh
To say she, too, is happy to be back.

Night-Skating

I skate on ice
At night and I
See how, like dice,
The ebony sky
Holds stars as white
As beads of rice.

Steel runners hiss;
They cross and criss
And trace the shapes
Of fleur-de-lys,
Or ring, or kiss
Upon the ice.

And in the bright
And moonlit night
Blooms of mist
Flower on lips,
As joyful cries
Fall and rise.

And in the trees
That stand beyond
The frozen pond
A silver breeze
Softly sighs,

While scrape and squeal
Of hissing steel
Make crumbs of ice
All glister like
Little stars
Beneath the feet.

Cold air is sweet;
Inhaling it,
I seem to eat
A spectral meat.
And I know this
Is winter bliss;
And I know this
Is winter bliss.

Death of a Snowman

I was awake all night,
Big as a polar bear,
Strong and firm and white.
The tall black hat I wear
Was draped with ermine fur.
I felt so fit and well
Till the world began to stir
And the morning sun swell.
I was tired, began to yawn;
At noon in the humming sun
I caught a severe warm;
My nose began to run.
My hat grew black and fell,
Was followed by my grey head.
There was no funeral bell,
But by tea-time I was dead.

The Magic Show

After a feast of sausage-rolls,
Sandwiches of various meats,
Jewelled jellies, brimming bowls
Of chocolate ice and other treats,
We children played at Blind Man's Buff,
Hide-and-Seek, Pin-the-Tail-on-Ned,
And then – when we'd had just enough
Of party games – we all were led
Into another room to see
The Magic Show. The wizard held
A wand of polished ebony;
His white-gloved, flickering hands compelled
The rapt attention of us all.
He conjured from astonished air
A living pigeon and a fall
Of paper snowflakes; made us stare
Bewildered, as a playing card –
Unlike a leopard – changed its spots
And disappeared. He placed some starred
And satin scarves in silver pots,
Withdrew them as plain bits of rag,
Then swallowed them before our eyes.
But soon we felt attention flag
And found delighted, first surprise
Had withered like a wintry leaf;
And, when the tricks were over, we
Applauded, yet felt some relief,
And left the party willingly.
'Good night,' we said, 'and thank you for
The lovely time we've had.' Outside

The freezing night was still. We saw
Above our heads the slow clouds stride
Across the vast, unswallowable skies;
White, graceful gestures of the moon,
The stars' intent and glittering eyes,
And, gleaming like a silver spoon,
The frosty path to lead us home.
Our breath hung blossoms on unseen
Boughs of air as we passed there,
And we forgot that we had been
Pleased briefly by that conjuror,
Could not recall his tricks, or face,
Bewitched and awed, as now we were,
By magic of the commonplace.

Hide and Seek

Call out. Call loud: 'I'm ready! Come and find me!'
The sacks in the toolshed smell like the seaside.
They'll never find you in this salty dark,
But be careful that your feet aren't sticking out.
Wiser not to risk another shout.
The floor is cold. They'll probably be searching
The bushes near the swing. Whatever happens
You mustn't sneeze when they come prowling in.
And here they are, whispering at the door;
You've never heard them sound so hushed before.
Don't breathe. Don't move. Stay dumb. Hide in your
     blindness.
They're moving closer, someone stumbles, mutters;
Their words and laughter scuffle, and they're gone.
But don't come out just yet; they'll try the lane
And then the greenhouse and back here again.
They must be thinking that you're very clever,
Getting more puzzled as they search all over.
It seems a long time since they went away.
Your legs are stiff, the cold bites through your coat;
The dark damp smell of sand moves in your throat.
It's time to let them know that you're the winner.
Push off the sacks. Uncurl and stretch. That's better!
Out of the shed and call to them: 'I've won!
Here I am! Come and own up I've caught you!'
The darkening garden watches. Nothing stirs.
The bushes hold their breath; the sun is gone.
Yes, here you are. But where are they who sought you?

Elaine's Story

This happened when I was eight years old.
I was wearing my silver bracelet
That Granny gave me for my birthday.
Mummy was not there. I did not know
Where she had gone. It was a dark day
And it smelled of Monday. In the hall
The telephone started to ring. And ring.
Daddy was at home. I don't know why.
He was a policeman then. Not now.
He stays at home and looks after us.
I saw him pick up the telephone.
Yes, he said, Yes. He said it again.
Then he said, I see. I don't think
He could see though. His eyes were like glass
Or more like ice. They began to melt
And I saw his face starting to break.
The pieces did not fall on the floor
But they did not seem to fit together
Like they ought to do. I felt frightened.
His face is better now, looks mended
But not the same. His eyes don't either.
Mummy did not come back home. I kept
Asking where she was but now I've stopped.
I've stopped asking anything. Granny
Said she is with Jesus and happy.
I pretended that I believed her.

Growing Pain

The boy was barely five years old.
We sent him to the little school
And left him there to learn the names
Of flowers in jam jars on the sill
And learn to do as he was told.
He seemed quite happy there until
Three weeks afterwards, at night,
The darkness whimpered in his room.
I went upstairs, switched on his light,
And found him wide awake, distraught,
Sheets mangled and his eiderdown
Untidy carpet on the floor.
I said, 'Why can't you sleep? A pain?'
He snuffled, gave a little moan,
And then he spoke a single word:
'Jessica.' The sound was blurred.
'Jessica? What do you mean?'
'A girl at school called Jessica,
She hurts— ' he touched himself between
The heart and stomach '– she has been
Aching here and I can see her.'
Nothing I had read or heard
Instructed me in what to do.
I covered him and stroked his head.
'The pain will go, in time,' I said.

Thelma

Thelma was a Brownie.
I never spoke to her
Although we spent a year together
In Standard Three.
I once followed her home
From the Brownie HQ.
There was honeysuckle in the gardens;
Songs of gramophones too.
The satchel she brought to school
Was made of expensive leather
And in her hair
She wore a slide of tortoiseshell.
We never spoke,
Not once in all that time.
It was a long spell
And is not over:
When I smell honeysuckle now
It is Thelma I smell.

Love

Is it like a carnival with spangles and balloons,
Fancy-dress and comic masks and sun-drenched
    afternoons
Without a cloud to spoil the blue perfection of the skies?
'Well yes, at first, but later on it might seem otherwise.'

Is it like a summer night when stock and roses stain
The silken dark with fragrance and the nightingale again
Sweetly pierces silence with its silver blades of song?
'I say once more it can be thus, but not for very long.'

Is it like a great parade with drums and marching feet
And everybody cheering them, and dancing in the street,
With laughter swirling all around and only tears of joy?
*'If that alone, you'd find the fun would soon begin to
    cloy.'*

Is it like the falling snow, noiseless through the night;
Mysterious as moonlight and innocent and bright,
Changing the familiar world with its hypnotic spell?
*'It has been known to be like that, and other things as
    well.*

*'But if you find, when all the brightest ribbons have
    grown frayed,*
The colours faded; music dumb, and all that great parade
*Dismissed into the darkness where the moon has been
    put out,*
*Together you find warmth and strength, then that's what
    it's about.'*

Miss Steeples

Miss Steeples sat close;
She touched me.
Her hands were white,
Fingernails pink,
Like shells of prawns.
They tapped my desk
And, as she murmured,
Numbers blurred.
She smelled of spring
And cool cash chemists.
One summer evening,
Not by chance,
I met her walking
Near the green
Tennis-court
She beautified
Dressed in white.
In one hand swung
A netted catch
Of tennis balls.
She smiled and said,
'Hello.'
She smiled.
Love-punctured
I could not answer.
At the end of the summer
She went away.
It was her smell I loved
And her fingernails.

Why?

They ask me why I love my love. I say,
'Why do summer's roses smell so sweet
And punctually put on their rich display?

'Why does winter lash the fields with sleet
And make cold music in the leafless trees
Yet strangely seem to warm our snug retreat?

'Why does moody April taunt and tease
With alternating sun and dancing rain?
Why do nettles sting the flesh like bees?

'Why are the stars tonight like silver grain
Broadcast on the far dark fields of sky?
Why does the owl rehearse its sad refrain?

'With loving, too: no point in asking why.
There is no answer.' That is my reply.

Waiting for the Call

Sitting in the curtained room
Waiting for the distant call,
Hearing only darkness move
Almost noiseless in the hall
Where the telephone is hunched
Like a little cat whose purr
May be wakened if you press
Ear against its plastic fur,
He sits and knows the urgent noise
Probably will not occur:
There's little hope and, if it does,
He's sure – almost – it won't be her.

Love Shouts and Whispers

Love shouts and whispers and it often sings,
And, even when the voice is hoarse or low,
It somehow manages to rise on wings
Of sweet and secret music and will grow
Lovelier as you listen through the years,
Though only audible to lovers' ears.

Love shouts out loud, exultant, in its youth,
And longs for all the world to recognize
That it may lead towards the well of truth
And lasting happiness if we are wise
And trust the compass-bearings of the heart,
Discarding cautious reason's careful chart.

Love whispers in the autumn evening's calm
But, though the voice is soft, the words are bright
And durable as diamonds. No harm
Will come to lovers in the prowling night;
And when white winter shakes its icy chains
Love whispers warmth that comforts and sustains.

Famous Lovers

Everyone has heard about
Romeo and Juliet,
And all those lovers long ago
We modern sweethearts can't forget.

Since you and I first fell in love
I've thought a lot about the old
Tales of famous couples whose
Stories are inscribed in gold.

I really mean in golden words
That please the heart and mind and ear,
Prose and poetry that tell
Of Lancelot and Guinevere,

Of Heloise and Abelard,
Tristram and Iseult: such names,
As Dido and Aeneas, gleam
And flicker in the dark like flames.

Mind you their owners seemed to come
To sticky ends. Maybe it's wise
For us to stay anonymous
And hidden from the public's eyes.

Though, come to think of it, I can't
Imagine that our names would be
Engraved eternally upon
The universal memory.

Kev and Tracey? I don't see
A poem here, I must confess,
Or a play. But don't think this
Is proof we love each other less.

Getting There

Call for a taxi, Maxie,
Or phone for a mini-cab;
Don't worry about the meter,
I'll gladly pick up the tab.

Ignore the doorman, Norman,
The cabbies are all on strike;
It's got to be Shanks's Pony,
Or getting on your bike.

Jump on the ferry, Jerry,
It sails on the morning tide;
All day the bars will stay open
On the port (and the sherry) side.

Leap on your cycle, Michael,
And zoom very fast, then display
The proper hand-signal for Norman,
Should you happen to meet on the way.

On to your scooter, Pooter,
As pompous as pompous can be;
The tin-tacks we've spread out will puncture
Your tyres and your vanity.

Into your Morris, Doris;
I wish I'd been given the chance
To join you; we'd park and together
Alight for a quick Morris dance.

Drive the jallopy, Poppy;
It's ancient but none of us care
How bumpy and lengthy the journey
As long as we get safely there.

Flying a Camel

'When I was young,' the old man said,
   'I joined the Flying Corps.
That, of course, was long ago
   In the First World War.

'I flew a Sopwith Camel then
   And liked it very much.'
'A camel!' said the little boy,
   'You're talking double-Dutch!'

'Not that kind! An aeroplane:
   It had two wings in front,
A biplane not a monoplane;
   Its nose was big and blunt.

'But it was marvellous to fly,
    Simple as a kite;
The joystick sent it up or down,
    The rudder left or right.'

'But why a camel?' said the boy,
    'Why not a horse, or whale?'
'I'm not quite sure – maybe because
    It had a rounded tail.

'I only know it was such bliss
    When I soared high above
The clouds and dived, and soared again,
    I felt a kind of love,

'The way a horseman feels his mount
    Respond beneath his hands
And knows his horse will never fail
    To answer his demands.'

The boy said, 'Did you fight a lot
    And knock the Jerries out?'
The old man then looked sad: 'That's not
    A thing I talk about.'

The Journey

'Hold tight! We are about to start!'
I feel the beating of my heart
Increase in tempo; then we glide
Away quite slowly. At my side
I hear my fellow-rider sigh
As she expels her breath, and I
Steel myself to undergo
The many perils that I know
We both must face. Already we
Have gathered speed and I can see
The world whizz by, all detail blurred.
My friend shouts out, but not a word
Reaches me, and faster still
We skid and speed uphill, downhill,
And, even faster, take a bend,
And then another, and ascend
Yet again at sizzling pace
And feel the wind in hair and face
Changed from breeze to hurricane
As all my nerves and sinews strain
Against the threat of being hurled
Out into the static world
Where surely I'll be smashed to pieces.
Then suddenly the tension eases
And the breakneck speed decreases
Until we're moving really slow;
And then we come to rest and know
The journey is completed; so,
On shaky legs, we walk away.

Where have we travelled to today?
Nowhere at all; and should you doubt
My word, or think that I am out
Of my small mind, let me explain:
Neither of us is insane,
And of course we have not lied –
We've just been on a switchback ride!

Beauty of Boats

The river's polished waters flow
And morning sun slips golden rings
On ghostly hands that drift below
As gulls extend sustaining wings.

And, nosing at the little quay,
The boats like tethered ponies play;
They nod and nudge and seem to be
Welcoming another day.

Canoes and skiffs, these simple craft,
Are beautiful: the graceful flow
Of that sweet line from fore to aft
Is like the glide of fiddle bow.

It floats a noiseless music in
The darkness of the listening heart.
A boat or silent violin
May please us like a work of art.

Each boat is built to serve a need:
The symmetry of that design
Is planned for buoyancy and speed;
Functional, that swooping line.

And yet it is a pure delight
To landsmen who regard a boat
As something built to please the sight,
Forgetting beauty makes it float.

For if it lacked that clean, well-bred
Look that pleases casual eyes,
If symmetry were forfeited,
The boat would flounder and capsize.

O White Ship on the Blue

O white ship on the blue
Enormous, foam-flecked sea;
O breeze that fills the sails,
Bring back my love to me.

O waves that heave and roll,
Convey him safely through
The treacherous latitudes;
Let no more tempests brew.

O white bird of the ocean,
Inscribe on salty air
This message for my darling:
The love I here declare

Will keep him safe from lurking
Dangers and alarms,
Until at last he anchors
In the haven of my arms.

Submarine

This is the world of the submarine
A wavering jungle, dark and green,
That sailormen glide through;
They eat and sleep in their steel case
For weeks before going back to base,
And never see the view.

And it is magical, this world,
With restless foliage and curled
Serpents of the deep;
Small living submarines swim near
With goggle eyes, then disappear
Like images in sleep.

The crew lives in eternal night,
Lit by harsh electric light,
Like travellers who ride
In coach or carriage through superb
Scenery, yet can't disturb
The blinds to look outside.

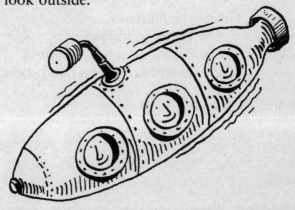

The Horse

Before men walked upon this earth
   And breathed the common air
In that primeval wilderness
   A kind of horse lived there.

Wise historians have claimed
   No men have ever made
Progress from the primitive
   Without the horse's aid.

Today there are so many breeds
   And types. I've never known
One that is not beautiful:
   The Palomino, Roan,

Arabian or massive Shire,
   Suffolk Punch and Bay,
The little Shetland, Welsh and Dale,
   As good at work as play.

Gentle, vegetarian,
   Intelligent and brave,
The horse for countless centuries
   Has been Man's friend and slave.

And, next to footprints on the trail
   From Man's dark hidden source
Towards the civilized, we find
   The hoofprints of the horse.

Pony Trap Rap

I've ridden in,
And on, most things
That you can think of:
Things with wings
And things with wheels,
Things with rudders,
Things with keels;
Buses, barges,
Tandems, trikes,
Scooters, skiffs
And motor bikes;
Rickshaws, sledges,
Skates and skis,
Vauxhall Vivas,
Ford Capris;
Helicopters,
Submarines,
Balloons and zeppelins,
Flying-machines;
Speed boats, schooners,
Once on a raft;
Canoes and ferry-boats,
Hovercraft.
I've ridden solo,
Pillion too;
I've soared so high,
Right out of view;
Sailed as a passenger
And as crew.
But there's one thing
That I must do

That I have never
Done before,
Something simple
I'd adore:
I long to drive
A pony and trap,
And hear the delicate
Tippety-tap
Of the pony's hooves
Down country lanes,
And sit up proud
And hold the reins,
And wear a billycock
Or flat cap;
I'd look a proper
Country chap.
I'd dump my compass
Rip up map,
And stay at home
Not care a scrap
As long as I had
My pony and trap;
As long as I had
My
      pony
          and
              trap.

Rolling Away

Lots of children must have thought:
   'What fun to run away!'
Most who try it, I would guess,
   Are back on the same day.

I knew a person once who chose
   To leave home for the cold
And lonely world beyond, but he
   Didn't run – he rolled.

He took his savings – 30p –
   Some biscuits, cheese and dates,
Then he sneaked out and rolled away
   On his new roller-skates.

It was a very special day –
   From that boy's point of view –
The day he'd reached the age of eight:
   That's why the skates were new.

He'd never owned a pair before,
   Though friends had let him learn
To skate on theirs, but now he'd no
   Need to wait his turn.

But why should he, you may well ask,
   Decide to roll away
From home and leave his mum and dad?
   I think that I can say:

You see, although he loved them both,
  He somehow knew he must
Seek unknown places; what he felt
  Is known as 'wanderlust'.

He did not reach the Amazon,
  Samarkand or Monterey;
In fact a policeman brought him back
  From a place four miles away.

He travelled in a Panda car
  And he was glad to be
Home in time to sit down for
  His scrumptious birthday tea.

Night Flight

For ages I have kept my secret. I
Have never told my mum or dad. She'd sigh
And say: 'Yes darling, very nice for you,'
And not believe a word. And, as for Dad,
He'd shake his head and say, 'It's time you knew
How to spot what is and isn't true,
And stop confusing dreams and fact, my lad.'

But you're my friend and we see eye to eye
So I'll confide my secret: I can fly.
I mean it. I can fly. It has to be
When everyone has gone to bed at night –
Not every night, but maybe one in three –
I get out of my bed and silently
Ease my window open and take flight.

I soar above the rooftops and the trees,
Choose whatever altitude I please.
And I have had some strange adventures too.
I see you don't believe me, but I swear
Two nights ago I ventured out and flew
Away from town to where some tall pines grew
And found a tawny owl had nested there.

Owls use discarded nests of birds like crows.
I peered inside for eggs – and then I froze
With terror as a feathered fury flew
From out of darkness, clawing at my eyes.
I turned and fled, but not before it drew
Some blood. You see the claw-mark? Now do you
Believe? You will if, owl-like, you are wise.

Kite Flight

A windy day on Crocker's Hill,
Cloud chases cloud across the sky;
Today my kite should heed my will;
Today's the day for it to fly.

And so it does: it soars up high,
Then briefly dips to rise again,
And I can see its pigtails fly
And feel the tight string's eager strain.

It pulls and jerks as if I held
An eager greyhound on a lead;
A mighty tug and I'm compelled
Almost to see the wild thing freed.

Not quite! I grip with all my might
And think for one mad moment I
Could be dragged upward by my kite
To dangle in astonished sky.

But no, there is a sudden lull;
The wind decides to stand at ease,
And like a swooping hawk or gull
My kite speeds down towards the trees.

Luckily, it skims their tops
And arrows back to Crocker's Hill;
It hits the ground, then twitches, flops,
A stranded fish, and then lies still.

Jam Roll in Custody

They took him to the local nick
    And put him in a cell.
I asked what charge was being brought,
    Although I knew quite well,
For I had handled similar cases
    With logic and with charm:
I specialize in G.G.H. –
    Grievous gastric harm.

My clients have included some
    Very shifty folk:
A ham burglar and shepherd spy,
    A rather half-baked bloke;
A trickster pushing jelly deals
    And lemon soles that trample;
A seafood Highlander, who set
    A rotten Scotch egg sample.

But I, with customary skill,
    Convinced the nodding judge
That Mr Bun, the plaintiff, bore
    All kinds of roll a grudge.
Jam roll was freed and we rejoiced;
    This pastry case was won.
The loser was enraged, of course;
    A very hot cross Bun.

Special Today

We can recommend our soups
    And offer thick or thin.
One is known as 'Packet',
    The other known as 'Tin'.

The flying fish makes a very fine dish;
    As good as plaice or skate
When sizzled in fat; but be certain that
    You tether it to your plate.

Now this hot dog makes an excellent snack;
    Our sausages are best pork.
If you can't get it down, please don't send it back,
    Take it for a nice brisk walk.

Are you tempted by our fried fish fingers?
    The last customer to succumb
Was hard to please; he demanded
    Why we couldn't provide a fish thumb.

Bubble and squeak is splendid stuff,
    And Chef takes endless trouble.
But if you feel you'd like a change
    Then try our squeak and bubble.

If you choose our historical steak
    You'll chew and chew and chew
And know what Joan of Arc,
    When tied to one, went through.

You may have tried most kinds of pie
    But have you ever dared
To munch a circular portion of
    Crusty πr^2?

Try our cabinet pudding
    Or a slice of home-made cake;
We serve with each, quite free of charge,
    A pill for your belly ache.

The Day That Summer Died

From all around the mourners came
The day that summer died,
From hill and valley, field and wood
And lane and mountainside.

They did not come in funeral black
But every mourner chose
Gorgeous colours or soft shades
Of russet, yellow, rose.

Horse chestnut, oak and sycamore
Wore robes of gold and red;
The rowan sported scarlet beads;
No bitter tears were shed.

Although at dusk the mourners heard,
As a small wind softly sighed,
A touch of sadness in the air
The day that summer died.

Incendiary

That one small boy with a face like pallid cheese
And burnt-out little eyes could make a blaze
As brazen, fierce and huge, as red and gold
And zany yellow as the one that spoiled
Three thousand guineas' worth of property
And crops at Godwin's Farm on Saturday
Is frightening – as fact and metaphor:
An ordinary match intended for
The lighting of a pipe or kitchen fire
Misused may set a whole menagerie
Of flame-fanged tigers roaring hungrily.
And frightening, too, that one small boy should set
The sky on fire and choke the stars to heat
Such skinny limbs and such a little heart
Which would have been content with one warm kiss
Had there been anyone to offer this.

Child with Toy Sword

Clutching in hero hand that bright
Symbol of death and glory,
He marches bravely to the fight
And grows as tall as a story.

The garden birds blow bugles for
His joy as he advances;
The sun declares a playful war
And throws down flashing lances.

And no one whispers to the boy
That some hot future afternoon
He will lunge upward with that toy
And burst the sun like a huge balloon.

Jason's Trial

Jason was a football freak;
  He really loved the game:
To be a first-class footballer
  Was his one aim.

He practised every day and played
  Again each night in dream;
When he was twelve they chose him for
  The school's first team.

He was quite brilliant. Five years passed
  And – though rarely this occurs –
It seemed his dreams might all come true:
  He was given a trial by Spurs.

He played a blinder on the day;
  The spectators cheered and roared,
And after the match he was asked to appear
  Before the Selection Board.

The Chairman said, 'I've got the reports
  From our experts who watched you play:
Your speed and ball-control were fine;
  For tackling you get an A.

'And when our striker scored his goal
  You were first to jump on his back
And when *you* scored you punched the air
  Before you resumed the attack.

'So far, so good; but you were weak
   On the thing our lads do best;
It seems you hardly spat at all,
   So you failed the spitting-test.

'But don't despair. If you go home
   And practise every day
You still might learn to spit with style
   In the true professional way.'

Peerless Jim Driscoll

I saw Jim Driscoll fight in nineteen-ten.
That takes you back a bit. You don't see men
Like Driscoll any more. The breed's died out.
There's no one fit to lace his boots about.
All right son. Have your laugh. You know it all.
You think these mugs today that cuff and maul
Their way through ten or fifteen threes can fight:
They hardly know their left hand from their right.
But Jim, he knew: he never slapped or swung,
His left hand flickered like a cobra's tongue
And when he followed with the old one-two
Black lightning of those fists would dazzle you.
By Jesus he could hit. I've never seen
A sweeter puncher: every blow as clean
As silver. *Peerless Jim* the papers named him,
And yet he never swaggered, never bragged.
I saw him once when he got properly tagged –
A sucker punch from nowhere on the chin –
And he was hurt; but all he did was grin
And nod as if to say, 'I asked for that.'
No one was ever more worth looking at;
Up there beneath the ache of arc-lamps he
Was just like what we'd love our sons to be
Or like those gods you've heard about at school . . .
Well, yes, I'm old; and maybe I'm a fool.
I only saw him once outside the ring
And I admit I found it disappointing.

He looked just – I don't know – just ordinary,
And smaller, too, than what I thought he'd be:
An ordinary man in fact, like you or me.

First Fight

I

Tonight, then, is the night;
Stretched on the massage table,
Wrapped in his robe, he breathes
Liniment and sweat
And tries to close his ears
To the roaring of the crowd,
A murky sea of noise
That bears upon its tide
The frail sound of the bell
And brings the cunning fear
That he might not do well,
Not fear of bodily pain
But that his tight-lipped pride
Might be sent crashing down,
His white ambition slain,
Knocked spinning the glittering crown.
How could his spirit bear
That ignominious fall?
Not hero but a clown
Spurned or scorned by all.
The thought appals, and he
Feels sudden envy for
The roaring crowd outside
And wishes he were there,
Anonymous and safe,
Calm in the tolerant air,
Would almost choose to be
Anywhere but here.

II

The door blares open suddenly,
The room is sluiced with row;
His second says, 'We're on next fight,
We'd better get going now.
You got your gumshield, haven't you?
Just loosen up – that's right –
Don't worry, Boy, you'll be okay
Once you start to fight.'

Out of the dressing room, along
The neutral passage to
The yelling cavern where the ring
Through the haze of blue
Tobacco smoke is whitewashed by
The aching glare of light:
Geometric ropes are stretched as taut
As this boy's nerves are tight.

And now he's in his corner where
He tries to look at ease;
He feels the crowd's sharp eyes as they
Prick and pry and tease;
He hears them murmur like the sea
Or some great dynamo:
They are not hostile yet they wish
To see his lifeblood flow.
His adversary enters now;
The Boy risks one quick glance;
He does not see an enemy
But something there by chance,
Not human even, but a cold
Abstraction to defeat,

A problem to be solved by guile,
Quick hands and knowing feet.
The fighters' names are shouted out;
They leave their corners for
The touch of gloves and brief commands;
The disciplines of war.
Back in their corners, stripped of robes,
They hear the bell clang one
Brazen syllable which says
The battle has begun.

III

Bite on gumshield,
Guard held high,
The crowd are silenced,
All sounds die.
Lead with the left,
Again, again;
Watch for the opening,
Feint and then
Hook to the body
But he's blocked it and
Slammed you back
With a fierce right hand.
Hang on grimly,
The fog will clear,
Sweat in your nostrils,
Grease and fear.
You're hurt and staggering,
Shocked to know
That the story's altered:
He's the hero!

But the mist is clearing,
The referee snaps
A rapid warning
And he smartly taps
Your hugging elbow
And then you step back
Ready to counter
The next attack,
But the first round finishes
Without mishap.

You suck in the air
From the towel's skilled flap.
A voice speaks urgently
Close to your ear:
'Keep your left going, Boy,
Stop him getting near.
He wants to get close to you,
So jab him off hard;
When he tries to slip below,
Never mind your guard,
Crack him with a solid right,
Hit him on the chin,
A couple downstairs
And then he'll pack it in.'

Slip in the gumshield
Bite on it hard,
Keep him off with your left,
Never drop your guard.
Try a left hook,
But he crosses with a right
Smack on your jaw
And Guy Fawkes' Night

Flashes and dazzles
Inside your skull,
Your knees go bandy
And you almost fall.
Keep the left jabbing,
Move around the ring,
Don't let him catch you with
Another hook or swing.
Keep your left working,
Keep it up high,
Stab it out straight and hard,
Again – above the eye.
Sweat in the nostrils,
But nothing now of fear,
You're moving smooth and confident
In comfortable gear.
Jab with the left again,
Quickly move away;
Feint and stab another in,
See him duck and sway.
Now for the pay-off punch,
Smash it hard inside;
It thuds against his jaw, he falls,
Limbs spread wide.
And suddenly you hear the roar,
Hoarse music of the crowd,
Voicing your hot ecstasy,
Triumphant, male and proud.

IV

Now, in the sleepless darkness of his room
The Boy, in bed, remembers. Suddenly
The victory tastes sour. The man he fought
Was not a thing, as lifeless as a broom,
He was a man who hoped and trembled too;
What of him now? What was *he* going through?
And then The Boy bites hard on resolution:
Fighters can't pack pity with their gear,
And yet a bitter taste stays with the notion;
He's forced to swallow down one treacherous tear.
But that's the last. He is a boy no longer;
He is a man, a fighter, such as jeer
At those who make salt beads with melting eyes,
Whatever might cry out, is hurt, or dies.

The Last Fight

This is one you know that you can't win.
You've lost your snap, can't put the punches in
The way you used to, belting till they fell;
You'll have a job to fiddle to the bell.
One round to go; backpedal, feint and weave;
Roll with the punches, make the crowd believe
You've still got something left. Above all, go
The distance, stay there till the end, although –
Even if you clipped him on the chin –
You know that this is one that you can't win.

The Cat's Tale

I have a cat called Tinkerbell;
    Have you one too?
And do you really love your cat?
    I bet you do.

But let me tell you something now
    You may not know:
In Egypt cats were holy things
    Millennia ago

And in the vaults of pyramids,
    And under sandy ground
Modern men found burial sites:
    And guess what else they found –

The mummies of old kings and queens
    (No, not their *mums*, you twit!)
And jars of various kinds of food
    In case they needed it.

As well as those dead kings and queens,
    And maybe princes too,
Little cats were mummified;
    I promise you that's true!

And here's a more amazing fact –
    Mice were mummified
In case the pussy mummies grew
    Hungry, though they'd died.

When I told this to Tinkerbell
  She stared with great gold eyes:
And in her gaze I saw my tale
  To her was no surprise.

For cats know more about these things
  Than people realize;
But they keep quiet, or softly purr,
  For they are very wise.

Night Cat

Sheba moves on velvet paws
Noiseless as a shadow or
Fall of one small feather on
The sleeping valley's mossy floor.

She becomes the night itself –
Once she is out and we in bed –
Night transformed to fur and claw,
Something smaller creatures dread.

From her blackness, like two moons
In miniature, her eyes alone
Declare her presence, gleaming bright
From where she crouches, still as stone.

But, at breakfast, we will find
Sheba on the carpet, curled,
Purring softly, tame and mild
In our human sunlit world.

The Apple-Raid

Darkness came early, though not yet cold;
Stars were strung on the telegraph wires;
Street lamps spilled pools of liquid gold;
The breeze was spiced with garden fires.

That smell of burnt leaves, the early dark,
Can still excite me but not as it did
So long ago when we met in the park –
Myself, John Peters and David Kidd.

We moved out of town to the district where
The lucky and wealthy had their homes
With garages, gardens, and apples to spare
Clustered in the trees' green domes.

We chose the place we meant to plunder
And climbed the wall and tip-toed through
The secret dark. Apples crunched under
Our feet as we moved through the grass and dew.

We found the lower boughs of a tree
That were easy to reach. We stored the fruit
In pockets and jerseys until all three
Boys were heavy with their tasty loot.

Safe on the other side of the wall
We moved back to town and munched as we went.
I wonder if David remembers at all
That little adventure, the apples' fresh scent.

Strange to think that he's fifty years old,
That tough little boy with scabs on his knees;
Stranger to think that John Peters lies cold
In an orchard in France beneath apple trees.

I Bit an Apple . . .

I bit an apple and the flesh was sweet:
Juice tingled on the tongue and from the fruit
Arose a scent that memory received
And in a flash raised ghosts of apple trees,
Leaves blistered with minutest bulbs of rain
Bewildering an autumn drawing room
Where carpets stained with unaccustomed shadow
Heard one old table creak, perhaps moved too
By some remembrance of a former time
When summer, like a lover, came to him
And laid amazing offerings at his feet.
I bit an apple and the spell was sweet.

Rhyme-Time

I know that poems do not have to rhyme,
And yet I've always liked to hear words chime.
I've noticed too, that in the world's design
Rhymes play their part, occurring all the time,
Not just in sounds but in the way the fine
Gestures of a tiny plant will mime
In miniature the flourish of a pine,
Proud and lonely on the hill's skyline;
Or how the bright refulgence of moonshine
Is almost echoed in the sheen of lime;
The way the hawthorn foams, a paradigm
For spindrift blossom on the dancing brine.
Oh yes, it's true, all poems do not rhyme
But of the things that I will treasure, nine
Times out of ten, the sound and objects sign
Themselves on memory and warmly twine
Around the heart and rhythms of the spine
Through using chime and echo.

                                        It's no crime –
As verbal savages in grime and slime
Of their poetic darkness whine – to climb
To transcendental heights or try to mine
Deep in mysteries equally sublime
By rungs or shafts of rhyme. I know that I'm
Old-fashioned but I'd never care to sign
A contract that debars the chiming line.
Finally, I ask, what sweeter rhyme
Than your close heartbeat keeping time with mine?

Lullaby

For Nancy, aged two

The house is silent.
Black-furred night is heaped against the window,
And one pale, luminous eye remarks
How slowly hours devour the light.
Sleep softly darling;
I shall keep three candles lit beside your bed,
Three golden blades will pierce the heart
Of night till morning finds him dead;
Sleep softly darling, sleep.

Index of First Lines

The very best poetry available from Macmillan

The prices shown below are correct at the time of going to press. However, Macmillan Publishers reserve the right to show new retail prices on covers which may differ from those previously advertised.

All Macmillan titles can be ordered at your local bookshop or are available by post from:

Book Service by Post
PO Box 29, Douglas, Isle of Man IM99 1BQ

Credit cards accepted. For details:
Telephone: 01624 675137
fax: 01624 670923
E-mail; bookshop@enterprise.net

Free postage and packing in the UK
Overseas customers; add £1 per book (paperback)
and £3 per book (hardcover)